Simeon Bolles

The Early History of the Town of Bethlehem, New Hampshire

Simeon Bolles

The Early History of the Town of Bethlehem, New Hampshire

Reprint of the original, first published in 1883.

1st Edition 2024 | ISBN: 978-3-38533-243-0

Verlag (Publisher): Outlook Verlag GmbH, Zeilweg 44, 60439 Frankfurt, Deutschland
Vertretungsberechtigt (Authorized to represent): E. Roepke, Zeilweg 44, 60439 Frankfurt, Deutschland
Druck (Print): Books on Demand GmbH, In de Tarpen 42, 22848 Norderstedt, Deutschland

THE

EARLY HISTORY

—OF THE—

TOWN OF

BETHLEHEM

NEW HAMPSHIRE.

—BY—

REV. SIMEON BOLLES,

WOODSVILLE, N. H:
ENTERPRISE PRINTING HOUSE.
1883.

PREFACE.

THE interest felt by many in preserving the early history of Bethlehem as well as the importance of these records and the opportunities for obtaining such information is annually decreasing. It was apparent that unless soon collected and put in form to be retained they would be lost to view in that darkness that follows close ly the march of time.

As no one seemed willing to undertake the task I have secured what facts I could in so short a time and I now present them to the public. The style of writing may vary but the facts presented lose none of their legitimate importance or interest.

S. B.

Bethlehem, August 3, 1883.

E. B. Wallace, Publisher and Printer,
Woodsville. N. H.

THE
EARLY HISTORY
—OF—
THE TOWN OF BETHLEHEM, N. H.

CHAPTER I.

WHILE some parts of our country are furnishing conclusive proof, in the form of mounds, fortifications and other relics of various kinds, that a race were dwellers in the Western World long before and superior to the red man in development, if not by nature, we have no proof that Bethlehem was ever inhabited or even known to exist by any human being prior to the existence of the North American indian; and we fail to find conclusive evidence that the red man ever chose this spot for a permanent home. No doubt the uncultivated children of the forest (being lovers of nature,) came at times to hunt and fish or to enjoy a few weeks of pleasure in nature's wild retreat, and it may be that these commodious

1

structures that furnish pleasant homes for the many tourists who annually visit this lovely spot, have been erected on the same grounds that were once utilized by the red man on which to construct his wigwam. Who can say that on the same identical spot beneath the overhanging branches of some forest king, in twilight hour, a wood-nymph being the only witness, the dark-skinned warrior did not woo and win his dusky mate?

While the mound builders were unconsciously making records that would reveal the fact to future generations that they once existed, that which is now Bethlehem was clothed with primeval upland grandeur beautified by nature's own adornments. No sound of the woodman's axe, no crack of the hunter's rifle, no merry laugh of happy children were heard and no familiar bell awoke the echoes of Sabbath morning calling the people to church. The morning and evening stars saw no change and setting sun bid adieu, (not a final farewell,) kissing tree-tops and hillside with his departing rays to greet them again on the morrow. Thus things continued without any essential change during periods of unknown length. Could an observer have been permitted to look upon this enchanting spot from his home on some planet far off in the regions of space, his thoughts might have been something like the following: "Thou Invisible One! Why such lavish display of Thy creative power in that uninhabited region with gradual sloping grounds, more conspicuous elevations, plats and valleys covered with forest kings with giant forms interspersed with various specimens of the floral kingdom? No human beings enjoy the beauties of this favored spot for none are there. Why is it thus?" Echo repeats, "Why?" and the sound dies away in ethereal space.

After the lapse of ages the question is answered. In harmony with the Creators wise arrangment of things his plans are gradually unfolded to the comprehension of man. Things created for the benefit of our race and the uses that the Creator designed that man should make of them, are made known to him as fast as man's upward progress and development require such knowledge. The North American indian had no use for oar, coal or petroleum stored away by their Creator beneath the surface of the globe and he knew but little or nothing of their existence. But when society became civilized and enlightened there were corresponding needs to be supplied, and in harmony with the Creator's plan mans knowledge of these hidden treasures, with ability to obtain and utilize them, was co-extensive with the demand for them. Crowded cities, close application to business and unhealthy climate necessitated rest, a change of scenery and atmosphere. While causes were creating a necessity for such a change, causes were preparing places where such changes could be obtained. Civilization was on the march, and hardy pioneers found their way to this hilly region, gradually the population increased and usurped the laws of nature and woodland glory disappeared before the stately tread of civilization. The hand of industry utilzed the primeval forest and flowing streams, while the virgin soil yielded an abundant harvest.

At this point we leave the subject and go back to an earlier date in the history of the town. It was early dawn in the beautiful morning when the feathered tribe were stopped and startled in the midst of their early songs, wild beasts were disturbed in their lairs and old Bruin sat upon his haunches, while the nimble squirrel ascended to the top-most branch of some stately tree to understand, if possible, the meaning of those strange

sounds and wonderful sights ; but being new to
them they could not solve the mystery, for they
now beheld for the first time, the camp of the
white man, with its ascending smoke ; they heard
the sound of the wood-man's axe as stroke after
stroke was vigorously applied, and the meaning
of all this was that the wild occupants of the for-
rest could no longer hold undisputed sway over
that part of natures wild domain ; and more, it
was the precursor of important events, a link in
the long chain of cause and effect by which the
Creator governs the world.   It was a harbinger of
the day when Bruin must live a more retired life
or retreat before the advancing tide, when game
of all kinds must for their own safety keep a
sharp lookout for their new but deadly foe, when
the beauties of well cultivated fiields would sup-
plant woodland glory, when log cabins would disappear before an increasing number of more com-
modius and better constructed framed buildings,
when school and meeting houses shuld dot the
place, standing like so many guardian angels to
protect the best interests of society, when rail-
roads, telegraph and telephone would connect
this town with Boston and other great cities,
when Bethlehem Street would witness the com-

never-failing springs, spread with great rapidity
along the borders of civilization and soon became
the theme of conversation at public gatherings,
with laboring men in their daily toil and at the
family hearth-stone; children sat on father's knee
to hear the wonderful story aud lovers gravely
consulted together as to the feasibility of beginning a wedded life in the promised land.

The first to awaken slumbering echoes by establishing permanent homes mid the grandeur of
primeval beauty, were Benjamin Brown and Jonas Warren from Massachusetts.   This was in
1787 or 1788.   For a time there were only three
families in town, the two above named and another the name of which, from whence they came,
how long they resided here, or whither they went,
we can find no trace.   Mr. Warren located on
the place now occupied by Charles Blandin; they
had four children, Otis, Betsy, Jonas and Anna.
Mr. Brown settled on the farm known as James
Bean place on the South Road.   They had eleven
children, named Abigail, Frances, Marcus, Benjamin, Ida, Cynthia, Anna, Susannah, Triphena,
Oliver and Mahala.   Marcus died in Bethlehem
leaving one son and one daughter who now reside in town.   Two of the eleven children above

named, Benjamin and Ida were twins, the first pair born in town.

In the spring of 1790 James Turner began his settlement on Lloyd's Hill, there being at that time only two families in town; afterwards during the same year others came. In March, 1794, Lot Woodbury settled in town, he came from Roylston, Mass., bringing his family and effects on an ox sled.

The shorter month of February had lived out its time and the longer days of March with their piercing cold were now in line of march following closely its predecessor. The ground was clothed in its pure white garments so beautifully adapted to the winter season in this northern clime. The rippling brook and murmuring rill were hushed in silence bound by fetters of ice and clothed with a silvery sheen. The cold breath of frozen north with icy coldness penetrating every nook and corner. Its chilling influence caused fond mothers to be more careful of their little ones and travelers instinctively wrapped more closely around themselves their outer garments. Snow birds continued to come daily to doors and windows of friendly dwellings in quest of food in the form of bits of bread or cold potatoes from the remnants of a well-spread table that chanced to find its way to the exterior of the buildings, and occasionally. a group of little children with eyes sparkling with delight and showing extreme pleasure, might have been seen with busy hands fetching crumbs to their charming little visitors, while a solitary crow might have made his presence known by his accustomed "haw," moving lazily on the wing as if in search of food or signs of warmer weather ; but the time had not come for the warm blushes of spring to dispel that frigid look that covered the face of Nature.

In the town of Roylston, Mass., at the time of which we are writing, there might have been seen an unusual stir that showed conclusively that an important event was near at hand not unlike those scenes transpiring to a greater or less extent along the borders of civilization. Neighbors gathered at this central point of attraction not to converse on the general topics of the day, but to share in those scenes and witness those events in which they felt a special interest , no pleasing story was rehearsed or jovial language used, no merry peals of laughter or songs of mirthful import saluted the ear, but solemnity bended over this little group of anxious friends, for their hearts were sad and their eyes were filled with flowing tears.

The wood in the old fashioned fire-place had not been replenished for some little time, the large fore-stick and huge back-log had been converted into glowing embers by the devouring element and a small tallow candle was burning low in its iron socket, whose dim and flickering light gave a dreary aspect to various objects within the room, harmonizing with the feelings of the little company. Warm grasping of hands, a fervent parting kiss, and ejaculations of "my best wishes I leave with you," "don't forget us," and "may God bless us all" ends the scene within. Before the door of the dwelling stood a yoke of oxen attached to a sled on which might have been seen household effects, provisions, and a small amount of farming implements, the family now coming forward taking their allotted seats, the load was completed,when all being ready the team moved on. The sky was cloudless and the twinkling stars still shown in all their glory for twilight had not come to dim their heavenly beauty.

Slowly and silently the subject of our narative moves onward and when day dawned they were beyond the sight of their once happy home

This family consisted of Lot Woodbury and wife, one pair of twins named Zariah and Oliver, about two years old, and Asa about six weeks of age. Asa died in this town loved and respected by all who knew him, being a prominent man and a good citizen, leaving behind him an influence for good which none but a kind, benevolent, true-hearted, and practical Christian can. We can picture in our imagination the feelings and emotions of those anxious parents as they journeyed in the twilight of morning; fields and gardens were being left in the rear, familiar objects and loving friends had been seen by them (it might be for the last time) and the certainty of what they left behind and the uncertainty of that which was before them made it a moment of intense interest to those thoughtful travelers.

While contemplating the hardships that awaited them in their forest home, the possible dangers from wild beasts, cold, and hunger, they were cheered with the thought that warm hearts and welcome greetings awaited them on their arrival. As the cold increased with the rising sun the fond mother cared for the twins as best she could, at the same time hugging her babe more closely to her throbbing bosom. Slowly and wear-

ily the day wore on, night was approaching, twilight came silently on as the brightness of day
begun to recede. The sun had gone to rest in
its far off western home, giant forms stood mo-
tionless in the piercing cold of the evening air,
while their branches moved to and fro like spec-
tral forms in a stirring breeze far in the frozen
north, but the children heeded it not being wrapped in bonds of quiet slumber. In a short time a
comfortable shelter was secured for the night
and thus ended the first day's journey.

In the morning, refreshened in body and spirits, they continued on their way. Day after day
they moved slowly on surrounded by the same
general scenery, good and poor roads, forests
and cultivated patches of land with here and
there a lonely dwelling, hills and valleys met
their sight, while the sameness of the teamster's
voice and language, the likeness of the cries and
prattling noise of the little ones and calm, soothing voice of the fond, careful mother all combined to make their long tedious journey a monoto-
nous one.

In due time they reached the brook in the
little valley about a mile west of Bethlehem
Street and began to ascend the hill. The oxen,

weary and worn by the heavy load they had
drawn and great distance they had come, moved
on mindful of the fact that the end was near,
but by much and constant urging with a vigorous given imperative command of "Gee Star,"
"Haw Line," or "Wake up my boy," which awoke
many slumbering echoes, the jaded team was in-
duced to obey the driver's voice and to move on,
stopping every four rods to rest.

The knowledge of their near proximity to their
future place of residence acted on the minds of
Mr. and Mrs. Woodbury like magic power: for
the moment forgeting their hardships and weariness of body and mind, they were exultant
with joy at the near realization of their long
cherished hopes. The children seemed to catch
the inspiration, for the twins talked more gladful
in their childish way and baby came in for a
share with an increasing prattle. In their frame
of mind the parents descanted on beauties of
Nature that surrounded them on either side, and
so charming to them was the scenery that Mrs.
Woodbury likened their journey up the hill to
that of ascending the hill of Zion. They soon
reached their place of destination. Halting before the cabin door of Jonas Warren where

they were to stay until a home of their own could be prepared.

The twins referred to in this narrative were the first brought to Lloyd's Hill. The only surviving member of Lot Woodbury's family is widow Wilder, the mother of Horace W. Wilder, the proprietor of the popular Centennial House. Mrs. Wilder was born in Bethlehem, which place has been her home up to the present time: she is the oldest person born in the town who is living there. She is cared for by her son Horace W. The 'oldest person in town is Isaac Newton Gay, born in Massachusetts in 1796.

The part that Mrs. Woodbury acted in establishing a new home in a distant forest seems more like the work of vivid imagination than of stern reality, but from the landing of the pilgrims on the ice-clad Rock of Plymouth, bold and brave women were ready to share in all the privations of a pioneer life. To much cannot be said in praise of those women who acted so conspicuous a part in laying the foundation for the future prosperity of Bethlehem. They were not only resolute and fearless but also persons of strong mind with good moral, christian character. They faithfully performed their duties as wives,

mothers and daughters at the same time render-
ing material aid in clearing, putting seed
in the ground in the spring-time and in
gathering their scanty harvest in the autumnal
season; in fact there was no labor in which they
did not have a hand to a greater or less extent.
The light and cheer imparted by the females of
those early times was not confined alone to their
own cabins, but it extended to every family in
the little settlement, they imparted life to social
gatherings, and their hopeful word and strong,
sympathetic feelings imparted comfort and new
life to the sick and disheartened. The names
and deeds of those self-sacrificing women, who
so patiently and heroicly contended with great
hardships and perils in planting the germ of civilization and in fostering the growth of enlightened society amid the the primeval forests that
then covered our now well-cultivated uplands and
valleys, deserve to be held in grateful remembrance by those who now enjoy the benefits of
their labors and when the last vestige of their
noble deeds shall have disappeared and time
shall have rendered epitaphs illegible and even
the headstone has crumbled and lost its identity
in the great whole from which it was taken, and

while the undying influence of those truly noble
women shall silently continue to work out its glorious mission, may recollections of them be en-
graven on the mind to the latest posterity.

Isaac Newton Gay came into town in 1800.
Of a Balm Gilead tree near the residence of A.
S. Phillips, Mr. Gay says, "On my seventh birth-
day, June 6, 1803, I set it out with my own
hands; there were two of them, but one died."
Nathaniel Snow, father of the Nathaniel Snow
who died in this town, originally surveyed Bethlehem, and the compass used is now in the pos-
session of Reuben Baker.

CHAPTER 3.

BETHLEHEM was incorporated Dec. 27, 1799. It
was originally called Lloyd's Hill; the first town
meetings were in 1800, and the following are
copies of their records:—

At a legal meeting of the legal voters of the
town of Bethlehem, held on Tuesday, the fourth
day of March, A. D. 1800, voted as follows:—

Sworn 1. Made choice of Moses Eastman for
a moderator.

Sworn 2. Made choice of Moses Eastman for
a Town Clerk.

Sworn 3.   Made choice of Moses Eastman for the first select man.

Sworn 4.   Made choice of Nathaniel Snow for the second .ditto.

Sworn 5.   Made choice of Amos Wheeler for the third ditto.

Sworn 6.   Made choice of Edward Oakes for a Constable.

Sworn 7.   Made choice of Edward Oakes for a collector.

Sworn 8.   Made choice of Simeon Burt for a Highway Surveyor.

Sworn 9.   Made choice of John Gile for a Highway Surveyor.

Sworn 10.   Made choice of Edward Oakes for a Highway Surveyor.

Sworn 11.   Made choice of Lot Woodbury for a fence viewer.

Sworn 12.   Made choice of Amos Wheeler for a Sealer of weights and measures.

Sworn 13.   Made choice of James Noyes for a Tithing-man.

Sworn 14.   Made choice of John Russell and Edward Oakes for hogreefs.

15.   Voted to dissolve the meeting.

A true copy,

attest, Moses Eastman, T. Clerk.
Moses Eastman, Moderator.

At a legal meeting of the legal voters of the Town of Bethlehem, held on the tenth of April, 1800, voted as follows, viz:—

1st.   Made choice of Edward Oakes for a moderator.

2nd.   Voted to raise Twenty-four dollars for Schooling.

3rd.   Voted to raise four dollars to defray Town charges.

4th.   Voted to raise Sixty dollars to be worked out on the road.

5th.   Voted to raise twelve dollars to defray Town charges.

6th.   Voted to dissolve the meeting.

Edward Oakes, Moderator.

A true copy,

Attest, Moses Eastman, T. Clerk·

At a legal meeting of the legal voters of the town of Bethlehem, held on May the 8th, A. D. 1800, voted as follows:—

1st.   Made choice of Lot Woodbury for a moderator.

2nd.   Voted to raise three hundred and ninety dollars to repair Highways and Bridges.

3rd.   Voted to allow eight cents per hour for

each man and six cents per hour for each yoke of oxen.

4th.　Made choice of Lot Woodbury, Amos Wheeler, Isaac Batchellor, Simeon Burt and Nathaniel Snow as a committee to look out a place where to build a bridge over Ammonoosuc River above Wm. Houghton's mills.

5th.　Voted that each man shall appear on the Burying ground on Wednesday, the fourth of June next, to clear and fence said ground.

Lot Woodbury, moderator.

A true copy,

Attest, Moses Eastman, T. Clerk.

CHAPTER 4.

LOVE of wild scenes and exciting adventures as well as a desire to acquire wealth caused immigration hither to continue, and various parts of New Hampshire and border states were represented by men and women of strong mental powers and great physical strength in this growing settlement. Increase of population was not confined to immigration, children were born here at an early date. Inquiring and curious

minds love to penetrate the far off past, and from
the gradually thickening gloom gather relics of
by-gone days. However interesting recent events
may be, there is a charm in those gleamings
wrenched from the relentless hand of decay or
snatched from the iron grasp of obscurity.
Nearly a century ago there might have been seen
in Bethlehem a lonely cabin surrounded on all
sides by dense forests, a mere speck in that comparatively unknown wilderness. There was nothing peculiar in this rude structure, being in
material, plan of make and general features
like all cabins erected by the pioneers of civilization. What a scene for a painter's brush! A
home with walls of unsmoothed logs shaped and
fitted by the woodman's axe; the roof like the
walls, was of rough material being made of poles
and covered with bark in which might have been
seen an uncovered spot through which the curling
smoke might pass in its ethereal wanderings.
The aspect of the interior of this dwelling was
much like the exterior, rough and unadorned;
no carpeted floors or walls adorned with paint,
paper or works of art, and no centre table laden
with poems, histories or popular novels, organs
and pianos were alike strangers in this woodland

but happy home.   Now additional joy has been added to former happiness and new pleasures suffuse the entire household.   New hopes and fears have found a place in their meditations and conflicting emotions reveal their existence in looks and actions.   Welcome sights greet the eyes of happy parents and pleasant scenes come like music to the ear.   A babe was born, the child of Mr. & Mrs. Benjamin Brown, whose name was Abigail, the first child born in this town.   As cares and anxiety increased naturally the mother contemplated the liabilities and probable events that would attend the progress of her little one from the cradle to mature years, and with true motherly instinct she anticipated the training of her new charge to fill with credit the responsible position she might be called upon to occupy in after-life.   She hoped to be able to impart to her daughter all the information and skill in those branches of industry so necessary for women to have in those early times.   They were expected to know how to convert raw material into needed food and clothing.   A young lady that could not with success roast potatoes, make bean porridge or bake on a board before a roaring fire, a corn-meal cake, or could not skillfully use the cards, convert toe and flax into yarn, weave it into cloth and make it into garments, patch, darn, or, milk a cow, was regarded as having a very imperfect education and not prepared to cope with real hardships and the ever-changing fortunes of life.

We now change locations, retaining essentially like scenes, and go to the cabin of Jonas Warren, to whom a son was born, named Otis, this was the first male child born in Bethlehem. With pleasure and joyful anticipations those happy parents looked forward to the time when developed physical strength and unfolded mind would fit their son to share in the laborious work of applying the axe, piling logs and clearing land, be a blessing to the household and occupy an honorable position in society. New hopes cheered them in their daily toil and many dark clouds that skirted the horizon ominous of coming evil, disappeared before the rising sun of prosperity.

Those hardy, self-denying pioneers, dwellers in their humble home, were destined to share the common lot of all our race. No constitution so strong or physical power so great that it will not yield to the great Creator's mandate. Mrs. Whipple sickened and it became apparent that she must soon bid farewell to loving friends, yielding to that inherent principle of decay which is a constituent part of all organic life. The angel of mercy, a never-failing friend of suffering humanity came to the afflicted family bringing the cheerful thought that the fatal moment might be long delayed, but hope and love could not roll back the gathering gloom soon to gradually deepen into darkness of death. One last, lingering look, one more soft pressure of the hand, a faint "Good bye," a gasp, the heart no longer beats, all is silent as death itself. She had gone beyond, passing through the mystic gate to that which is to us comparatively unknown, we call it Eternity. The antagonistical principles of life and death had long and strenuously contended for the mastery, but the latter finally triumphed, which must always be the result in all like conflicts. Life ceased to animate that once active form, death followed as a natural result; life and death are opposite to each other, death is when the life that was, is not.

Amid the wild grandeur of Nature's scenery, loving friends with tearful eyes and sorrowful hearts silently consigned the cold, inanimate form to the mother Earth and all that was visible disappeared from sight. But the invisible, that impress of character and influence left on the family circle, and to a greater or less extent on all their associates, can never die.   Seeds of morality and christianity sown by an affectionate mother and loving wife must silently but unceasingly work out their important mission, producing a legitimate harvest through rolling ages, and in that boundless expanse, that immeasurable and fathomless unknown, that which had its beginning in a rudely constructed cabin, must continue to fulfill its mission through the cycles of eternity.   This was the first death in Bethlehem, and on a tombstone, worn by the ravages of time in the old burying ground on the street, are the following inscriptions: Mrs. Lydia Whipple, died March 17, 1795; Mrs. Elizabeth Warren, died March 6, 1797.

CHAPTER 5.

THE first inhabitants of Bethlehem shared the lot common to all first settlers.   There were cabins to be erected, a heavy growth of timber to be removed and the soil to be prepared to receive the seed. To do all this required time. As the annual productions of the soil for the first few years must necessarily have been far below the demand, a large portion of the food used must have been supplied by forest and streams, and when every effort had been made to secure suitable sustenance they were forced to live on humble fare and none too much of that, even when prepared with skill and economy by a prudent housewife.

To be secure from cold, hunger and wild beasts, who were constantly on the alert to invade their barnyards, pigstyes and harvest grounds, was paramount. The near proximity of hunger was no strange thing, and strong men and women shuddered at future prospects and increasing cold. The nearest place where grain could be obtained or ground into meal was in the town of Bath, a distance of about 25 miles from Bethlehem street.

It was the month of June, bright stars were preparing to veil their nightly splendors and ajar were the warning gates through which, softly and silently, were creeping rays of mellow light —harbingers of coming day—when a man of medium size, with a knapsack strapped to his back and trusty gun on his shoulder, stepped upon the threshold of a small log cabin surrounded on all sides by primeval forests. He was strong and muscular, and care had left its mark on his honest but sunburnt face. His garments, though made of coarse material, showed the skill of well-trained hands; his hat, though somewhat worn, gave evidence of having seen better days. He stopped a moment, as if to speak to some one within, and then stepping forth into the open air, in a low tone soliloquized thus: "It looks a little like rain. That belt of reddish color stretched across the eastern sky foretells a change in the weather, or I have failed to read correctly signs that precede coming storms in this hilly region;" and then, looking in the opposite direction, said: "It is a long way and may be I shall have to come back without it, but I must go; I see no help for it," and started off in a westerly direction. With quick but steady steps he soon passed through the clearing that was before him and was lost to view in the great forest beyond. Guided by marked trees and other familiar signs, fast becoming visible by increasing daylight, he commenced to sing, in a style peculiar to a woodman, the following:—

" I love to roam 'mid giant trees,
    And dwell in Nature's bowers,
  With silvery streams and pure cold springs,
    Adorned with fragrant flowers.

" I dearly love my mountain home,
    Its many cares and toils,
  I love to fish, to pile the logs,
    And till the virgin soil.

" I labor hard, day after day,
    Forgetful of my sorrow,
  My dreams at night are sweet with thoughts
    Of better times to-morrow.

" The bread I eat, the bones I pick,"—

The remainder of his song was lost, for at that moment a noise in close proximity stopped short his singing. Immediately bringing his gun to his shoulder, his eyes penetrating the thick growth of timber from which the noise came, he heard the sound fast dying out in the distance. He had been so absorbed is his own thoughts he did not discover old Bruin, who was quietly taking his morning nap beneath the branches of a stately maple and whose ears, being quicker than the woodsman's eyes, had been alarmed by strange sounds, and started off on double-quick time without waiting to find out who the intruder was.

Our hero gave one glance in the direction the bear had taken, exclaiming as he did so:

> " Good bye, good bye, my happy sir,
>   I 'm in a hurry now,
>   But we will meet some other day,
>   And then I 'll show you how."

So saying, he turned and walked away, none the worse for his early adventure.

Nature was in her most pleasant mood, clothed in her best garb and adorned in the most lavishing manner. Tall trees were conspicuous in the broad sunlight which was penetrating nook and corner and fastening itself on every available object; gentle zephyrs sighed in the thick foliage and wild flowers, catching the inspiring influence, gracefully bowed their heads to the passing breeze, while feathered songsters acted a conspicuous part in filling the air with their sweet melodies.

Amid such surroundings one might be led to exclaim: O, Nature! thou great enchantress; the embodiment of the visible beauty and material manifestations of the glory, wisdom and grandeur of the Great I Am, ever directing our

thoughts to the vastness, incomprehensibleness
and power of the Invisible, thy Creator!"

On reaching the Ammonoosuc river, the subject of our sketch crossed over on a large tree
that connected the two banks, directing his footsteps down the stream, making no stop until he
reached the town of Lisbon; here he halted and
seated himself at the foot of a large pine tree.
After placing his gun in an upright position
against the trunk of the same tree that he might
be able to grasp it at a moment's warning and,
removing the knapsack from his back, pausing a
few minutes to rest his weary limbs and while his
thoughts were busy about the inmates of the
humble home he had left at early dawn, he
opened his sack and soon had spread before him
his humble fare, which consisted of dried meat,
some cold potatoes and a slice of bread made of
that obtained by sifting bran the second time,
which he ate with a relish born of necessity and
a keenly sharpened appetite. No murmuring
thoughts disturbed his mind, no words of com-
plaint escaped his lips, but he felt very grateful
for this humble meal and was truly thankful that
his condition was no worse. Having finished his
repast and replaced his gun and knapsack, he

started on his journey and in due time reached his place of destination, which was the grist mil[l] in the town of bath.

The sun had passed the meridian when the woodsman, placing his newly-ground grist in his commodious knapsack, started homeward· Reaching the top of a small eminence a shor[t] distance from the mill, he turned his head to take a hurried glance at the western sky, as he did so with some anxiety on his countenance, he exclaimed; "I was right in my opinion this morning about the weather; I must hasten." And in another moment he was suiting actions to his words with increasing pace. He did not pause again until he reached the pine beneath whose shady branches he had eaten his frugal meal a few hours before; here he halted to rest and take another survey of the heavens.

The distant cloud that bounded his vision at the time he stopped to view the sky when not far from the mill had so increased in size that it now extended to the north and south as far as the eye could reach and was high up in the heavens. He was about to start when a frightened rabbit came hopping by, calling his attention to the ground, revealing the footprints of some large beast and his skillful eye at once told him that they had been made by old Bruin only a short time before, and which, for ought he knew, might at that very moment be in close proximity to him.

Being in a hurry he had no time to investigate, and, thinking it best to postpone an interview with his shaggy enemy, again started homeward.

The sweet loveliness of morning was fast disappearing, being suppressed by the more solemn grandeur of declining day and rapidly gathering showers, giant kings, nodded in the increasing breeze while their outstretched arms waved in graceful recognition of coming changes. The dense foliage trembled in anxious suspense, wild flowers were closing their petals while their tiny forms seemed to seek shelter beneath the thick shrubbery and interwoven, overhanging branches as if preparing for approaching rain and nightfall. The feathered tribe had retired to a place of safety except a few venturesome ones not caring for storms, and lovers of darkness could now be seen on the wing enjoying gloom. Having reached the locality now the site of Littleton village, our traveller recrossed the Ammoonoosuc at the same point and on the same tree used by

him in the morning. Guide-marks on the trees
were now partially obscured by the darkness that
covered the forest; but he had no doubt of his
ability to move in the right direction. He had
not proceded more than half a mile when a sud-
den flash of lightning lit up the tree-tops and in
a few moments a peal of thunder came rolling on
the clouds from no great distance in a westerly
direction. The shower was now at Haverhill and
lashing Warren Heights with maddened fury.
Fortunately for our traveller the shower at this
point divided, leaving between the two parts an
intervening space of considerable width that did
not receive the full force of the storm. As soon
as he became aware of this fact he felt assured
that if he could reach home before the two di-
visions united, which they might do at some
point to the east, all would be well. With those
thoughts he hastened forward as fast as his
weary limbs and the thick darkness would
permit.

The almost unceasing flash of lightening whose
light penetrated the now appalling darkness prevented him from losing his way. He had now
reached a point about a mile from home when
he became conscious that the neutral ground

over which he was passing was fast yielding to the powers of warring elements narrowing down to a mere line, and that he was near the spot where the divided shower would coalesce.

Giant trees were now bending before the blast which threatened to uproot and prostrate their noble forms. The forest was stripped of its foliage and hurled in all directions, while broken branches filled the air with their mutilated forms. Great drops of rain fell thick and fast on the carpet of green that covered the ground. Nearer and nearer from either side came the unceasing roll of deafening thunder, while at no great distance a blaze of light penetrated the heavens, showing that the electric current had split and ignited some large tree venerable with age. Howling wind, terrific thunder and wild confusion, lit up by lightning's vivid glare, all conspired to make more grand and sublime this mountain storm.

At the moment when the warring elements which had been marshalling their forces for a final struggle, came in contact in all the madness of their wild fury and rain began to fall in torrents, the traveller, whom we have followed through the day, entered the humble cabin from which he came at early dawn.

Benjamin Brown had returned to cheer an anxious wife with his presence as well as with the meal made from a peck of corn, which cost its market price at the grist mill in Bath and a journey of fifty miles.

Fanciful as it may seem, kind reader, that one would journey on foot a distance of fifty miles to obtain the meal of a peck of corn, nevertheless, it is true, as persons will testify who were born here or came with their parents to mingle with the trying scenes of pioneer life, who are now venerable with age. The contrast between a life in Bethlehem as it then was and now is, being so great and the time between the two so long that we cannot fully realize the dangers and great hardships surrounding every-day life and connected with every transaction pertaining to a home in a vast wilderness. The real struggle to sustain life in the cheapest and most simple way and in every manner their ingenious minds could devise, so familiar to them are to us unknown, and as we read the records of those far off days we have only a slight conception of what the reality must have been.

CHAPTER 6.

NAMES and worthy deeds of those who figured so conspicuously in their sphere of action are rapidly becoming obscured by gathering gloom that follows in the footsteps of advancing time. Not only are names and deeds lost to memory but those marks of respect erected to show the exact spot, the last resting place of loved ones are fast disappearing before the merciless power of unyielding fate. Not many years hence names, deeds, and once sacred graves will all be forgotten, and feet of careless strangers will thoughtlessly press the ground where once grew the fragrant flowers planted by loving hands and watered by many tears of sorrow. When a knowledge of those worthy sons and daughters, fathers and mothers, husbands and wives who so patiently and heroically endured the hardships and braved the dangers of a wilderness home shall have lost its place in memory and all historic record of them become obsolete, the last epitaph obliterated by the march of time, and the headstone which has stood so many years as

a faithful sentinel to guard the sacred spot shall
cease to be; then will all record of them be buried
forever in the darkness of oblivion. Inscriptions
may become illegible, the plain uncarved stone,
the marble slab engraved by skillful hands, and
costly monumental piles will crumble and pass
away, but influence never dies; and who can tell
to what extent those influences that germinated
in those early cabins are interwoven in the des-
tiny of our town? Notwithstanding the untold
hardships and many sufferings the first tillers of
the soil enjoyed life. The causes that would le-
gitimately produce happiness existed within
themselves; coming from the land of the de-
scendants of the Pilgrims they possessed many of
those qualities characteristic of the Pilgrim Fathers. They were an honest, industrious people,
applying all their energies to the accomplishing
of laudable objects and contented with the lot
they had chosen, they cheerfully performed their
daily labor. Peaceful and quiet were their hours
of slumber, undisturbed by those frightful de-
mons that might arise from idleness, overeating
too richly prepared food, or a conscience disturbed by many crimes. Not that this people
were perfect, but they had good intentions, de-

siring to know their duty and. then to do it.

They had strong minds and positive convictions, teaching their children that strict integrity, good habits, industry and economy were essential to success. A spirit of true friendship entered largely into the makeup of their happiness. Not a friendship that blossomed in prosperity and vanished on the first indication of adversity, that exhausted itself in sympathetic expressions and flattering words, but a friendship that bloomed in poverty and sorrow, that shone most conspicuously where it was most needed in the darkest hours of life. If one of their number .was sick or by accident disabled the neighbors would all go and do him a substantial kindness in cutting wood, sowing the seed, or gathering in his harvest. A knowledge of this fact was a powerful element in their every day life, for they were confident that if they or their's should be unfortunate neither of them would suffer or die of starvation, if the others could prevent it, and this feeling of security kept from their minds those fearful thoughts that otherwise would destroy present happiness and blight their fondest hopes. Sociability was an important factor in their eventful lives. When, at times, weary and despondent from many cares and heavy burdens, as any mortal would be in like circumstances, the social element would come to their rescue, like the green oasis to a weary traveller in a barren land, or when fear for a moment would reign supreme and their frail bark seemed to be at the mercy of every rolling wave on life's stormy sea, a social chat would be to them like a fertile gem in mid ocean to the storm-tossed mariner. Its influence had a power for good on the minds of that overtasked people. It would calm their tears, dispel their gloom and reinstate those bright gems—Hope, Confidence, and Cheerfulness— in their proper places. To be social was not an exception but the general rule. When or where they met, whether by appointment, invitation or otherwise, in field, forest, or at the hearthstone in their humble dwellings, the gladness expressed on their countenances and warm grasp of the hand (not the tip of the fingers), were conclusive proof of the existence of warm hearts and true, loving sympathy. Together they toiled and lived in the bonds of real friendship, sharing each other's joys and sorrows. Unlike those societies of to-day, the germ of which was planted one hundred years ago, that little settlement had no castes or dividing lines. No money-grasping misers, rich in land, stock and government bonds to domineer; no self-conceited petty tyrant to look upon the honest laboring class as mud-sills of society; no idlers infested those industrious homes. No dandy, with artificial polish, his lily-white hands covered with fancy colored kid gloves and clothed in all the styles belonging to his kind, was present to live on the earnings of honest toil, there being no necessity for that class of men.

This secluded settlement had not only the elements essential to happiness and development but they were free from those counteracting influences to which thickly settled localities are subjected.

CHAPTER 7.

THE desire to acquire and enjoy homes of their own being inherent in human nature, was as strong with our ancestors as with this generation and the necessity of marriage relations in accomplishing the desired object was as great then as now, and the circumstances under which love-making commenced and ended in matrimonial bonds were as varied in the days when our narrative commences as in future times.

In the spring time of 1760, in the town of Barnardston, in the state of Maine, at early dawn a man might have been seen coming from the dwelling which had been his place of abode. He was of medium size and well porportioned with a build that showed him capable of physical endurance, unmarried and about 28 years of age. He had brown hair, blue eyes, a frank open countenance in whose general features were distinctly seen strength of purpose and mind, intelligence and good character. With a large pack on his back,—as if expecting a long journey,— and firm step, the subject of our narrative walked on in the direction of his destination, and in due time reached the town of Hanover. It was one of those lovely days characteristic of New England spring-time; not a cloud to be seen, and the air was soft and delightful. The king of day was lavish in bestowing its cheerful influence on the already changing aspects of nature, vegetation was awaking from its long inac-

tive condition to begin anew a career of progress
and unfolding, while beasts and birds alike
showed that they, too, were receiving inspiration
from the loveliness of the heavens. It was past
mid-day, the sun was silently but rapidly nearing
its destination to shine in all its magnificent
splendor in the far off western sky; but our traveller took no note of swiftly passing time, being
absorbed in a line of thought in which he was
deeply interested, involving, as it did, his future
happiness and plan of action. Being unmarried
and having a practical turn of mind, he naturally
took a common-sense view of whatever he wished
to accomplish, which would direct his meditations thus:

" I will thoroughly examine the locality and if
half be true that has been reported of it, I in-
tend to make a permanent home in that land of
promise; but a good home, such as I contemplate,
means a great deal and to obtain such an one a
large amount of work must be done,—a heavy
growth of timber removed, land cleared, seed
sown and harvest gathered; also a barn and
cabin must be created. Well, I think I can do
all of this, for I am satisfied that my mind and
body are equal to the emergency.

"But this is not all that is needed to make a happy home. I shall want a partner for life, a companion to cheer me in my lonely hours, to speak words of comfort and encouragement in times of adversity. I shall need, yes, need,—for it is no boyish fancy,—a wife to care for those things pertaining to the inside of my cabin, and a loving heart and willing hands to administer to me in times of sickness. Yes, this is reasonable. I must have a wife!"

But,.at this point his line of thought was interrupted by an impression on his mind, received through the medium of that unseen, mysterious telegraphic communication that connects mind with mind, which caused him to look up. As he did so he saw at once the author of the dispatch, that a moment before had disturbed him in his reveries. It was a female whose eyes were fixed intent upon him. The instant our hero saw the lady she turned her head, as though unconscious of the near proximity of a stranger, and this quick movement of our heroine might have deceived the stranger had it not been for a deep blush that mantled her fair face and the evidence it gave. In an instant, with true womanly sagacity, she put on an unconcerned air moving

slowly on, as though the incident had not occurred. She was mounted on horseback and
riding down a cross-road, the junction of which
to the more public highway, was only a few rods
distant. She had been to visit friends and was
returning home,—was plainly but neatly attired,
rode gracefully, and the manner she managed
the spirited beast showed that she was well
skilled in the art of horsemanship, which was not
an uncommon thing in those early times.

What the feelings of a man would be to have a
beautiful female spring up in his pathway, as if
by magic power, at the very moment when he
had just decided that he must have a wife and
for aught he knew may have spoken his thoughts
so loudly as to be distinctly heard by his fair
friend, can be better imagined by the reader than
described by a pen.

In a few minutes the two strangers met face to
face, at the intersecting point of the roads and
in a gentlemanly manner he saluted her, in the
style peculiar to the times, and she returned the
salutation in a graceful way with a genteel bow.

At first the two inclined to be reticent, arising
on the one side from modesty and her peculiar
situation, on the other from an inclination not to

be too formal with strangers: but, as they journeyed on together (for they were going the
same way,) this failing, as if by mutual consent,
gave place to pleasant conversation.

The lady, with that instinctive quickness peculiar to woman, soon felt assured of the good
character and noble qualities of this handsome
stranger, and the sequel showed that she was
correct in her hasty conclusions.

Having formed a favorable opinion of this
young man her sympathy for him was at once
aroused; having a kind disposition and willing to
practice the golden rule, "Do unto others as
you would have them do to you."

. She generously offered to take his pack, which
offer he readily accepted for his load grew heavier as the day neared its close, and the pack
which he had carried from early dawn was de-
posited on the back of the horse in care of his
interesting companion.

Then and there was an opportunity for the rider to betray the man who had shown such confidence in her by giving loose rein to the fleet-
footed beast, leaving the stranger minus his
knapsack. But he had no fears of that and there
was no necessity of any.

Being a close observer of human nature he unhesitatingly came to the conclusion that his female friend was a superior woman in point of intelligence and those qualifications that make woman truly noble, and in after life she proved to him that he did not overestimate her real value.

The rays of the setting sun now lingered on the summit of distant hills, as if unwilling to take a final departure, but only for a moment, for twilight soon claimed the right to exhibit her beauty and loveliness, as the mellow light that follows closing day began to disappear before the coming shroud of night.

She halted before the door of a neat looking cottage, at the same time informing her friend that this was her home and that he could stay all night with the family, if he choose. Being under the necessity of securing lodgings soon, as daylight was now gone, and confident that the accommodations would be satisfactory, he accepted the invitation and walked in.

On the morrow he started on his journey.

The name of this lady was Parker, her husband having previously died leaving two children The name of the gentleman was James Turner.

The acquaintance which commenced at the junction of the two roads finally ended in marriage relations.

Mr. Turner reached Lloyd's Hill without any adventure worth revealing, and liking the place soon began work.

He was the third permanent settler in Bethlehem.

He worked on his land through the season, returning to Massachusetts to spend the coldest part of the winter, coming back in the spring to resume his labor. This course he followed for two or three years, not forgetting to patronize the house where he found such good accommodations and pleasant society on a former occasion, in the town of Hanover.

When all was ready Mr. Turner was married to Mrs. Parker and went to reside at the new home in Bethlehem, and the cabin was now made pleasant and cheerful (of which Mr. Turner was thinking at the junction of the two roads on a former occasion,) by the presence of the fair stranger who generously carried for him his well filled knapsack.

His union with Mrs. Parker was one of the most fortunate transactions of his eventful life, while his wife found a husband worthy to hold that relation with a truly noble woman.

Mrs. Turner was a blessing to not only her own household but the whole settlement. Her skill in horseback riding, which she acquired before her last marriage, to which we have already alluded, was of great advantage to her in the new condition of things in which she was placed, and the little community where she resided, for, there being no practising physician at hand, Mrs. Turner, for a period of a number of years,— whenever necesity required it, and that was frequently,—mounted a horse, took her saddle-bags of medicines and visited the sick, acting the part of nurse and doctress. Though not a regular physician, she did good service, being acquainted with the medicinal qualities of many articles. By daylight and in darkness, in sunshine and storm, she hovered like an angel of mercy about the bed of the suffering; her coming always was greeted with delight. The sunlight that beamed from her countenance, the kind words she spoke and the hope inspired in her suffering patients, rendered her an object of respect and love by all who needed her assistance.

Although contented with her new place of
abode Mrs. Turner was much attached to the
many kind friends at Hanover whom she had
left behind, to share with her husband the rudely constructed cabin in the bowers of nature.
As difficult as was a long arduous journey to
her former home and old associates, she was
equal to the emergency and was permitted to
behold again those many objects and friends so
interesting and familiar to her in former times.

But how unlike the mode of travel then to that
of to-day! Now the roads from Bethlehem street
to Hanover are comparatively good and with a
covered buggy, constructed in modern style,
drawn by spirited horses, one can pass to and
from those two places with ease and comfort; or,
if one chooses to go by rail, he can go and return
the same day, eating breakfast and supper at his
own table. But the mode of travelling by the
early settlers of this town was on foot guided by
marked trees, on horseback, or with an ox team.
In the last mentioned way Mr. and Mrs. Turner
made three visit to Hanover, she, on one of these
occasions, carrying in her arms a babe six weeks
old.

With the present facilities for journeying the mother of to-day can hardly realize the fatigue and weariness of a journey with an infant in her arms on an ox s'ed, of from 140 to 200 miles, as was the case with those kind but resolute and energetic mothers who lived in those early times, in respect to danger, toil and suffering, we really know but little.

Although much might truthfully be said in relation to those noble women who acted so conspicuous a part in planting the germ of civilization in our beautiful highland home, yet we have no doubt but that the mothers and daughters of Bethlehem to-day would have, had they lived in those early times, as faithfully fulfilled their mission.

But the circumstances that necessitated some of the education and practical training of the times of which we write have passed away and disappeared before development and progress. The women of to-day can with honor and credit fill the places allotted them by the great change in surrounding circumstances holding in grateful remembrance the worthy deeds and good qualities of their own sex, who have preceded them.

CHAPTER 8.

THE first manner of going to mill was on foot with grist on their backs; the next was to put the grain on the back of steers, walking by their side. But, at the time of which we write, some used sleds.

Early one morning in spring-time James Turner started for Bath to mill, with a yoke of wide-awake steers and sled. The morning was warm and pleasant, teamster and team were in good spirits and ready for the journey. With an occasional "Whoa boys!" the sled moved briskly on.

While Mr. Turner was making good progress, omens of a gathering storm was seen in the heavens; a gentle breeze from the south sighed among the branches of leafless tree-tops, and dark clouds wandered here and there, as if on some aerial mission, like scouts on an advancing host, while the wind as if inspired by knowledge of coming events moved with increasing vigor amid the visible, craggy peaks of neighboring mountains, a prelude to a warm rain and coming thaw.

Mr. Turner was acquainted with these signs and understood their import. He knew that if the storm should burst in its fury before he could recross the Ammonoosuc on his way home, he might find himself surrounded with unpleasant and dangerous circumstances and, with hope and fear each in turn filling his mind, he made his way as fast as possible to his place of destination, which he reached without unnecessary delay or serious accident.

When everything was in readiness he started homeward. The atmosphere was now quite warm, with an increasing southerly wind and copious fall of rain. The snow was rapidly disappearing and soon water began to cover the ice in the river. He saw the danger and knew that his safety depended on the speed of his team. Soon an additional noise startled him, not because it was so loud or frightful, but it revealed the fact that jack frost was forced to succumb. The ice in the river was preparing to break, but at the same time he was aware that the catastrophe must necessarily be delayed for awhile.

The team received new impulse from the earnest tone of the teamster's voice, and all shared in the increasing excitement.

Faster went the steers, quicker and louder came the sound of breaking ice which finally mingled with a roar and a sound of rushing waters. Glancing backward his quick eye comprehended at once his true situation. A short distance below him the river had become obstructed, turning the ice and water into the road only a a few rods in his rear, and it was rapidly approaching to a dangerous proximity. It was now a race for life The roaring waters and mingling sounds of roaring elements so terrified the already much excited steers, that they strained every nerve to escape the jaws of death that were opened wide to receive them. The water, as if infuriated by its own exertions, receiving an impetus from the prospects of soon engulphing every object in its pathway, now increased in sound, volume, and rapidity of movement. While the manly form of Mr. Turner might have been seen as, in a voice distinctly heard above the confused mass of mingling sounds, he cheered his cattle on. It was a moment of great anxiety, for in that short space of time would be decided the question of life or death. Could they reach a point but a few rods distant all would be well, as at that place the ground began gradually to rise.

A misstep of one of the steers and all would be lost. No accident occurred; they were saved, and at nightfall he reached the usual place of crossing at the point now covered by Littleton village.

The river was so swollen he did not think it advisable to attempt to cross. There was one cabin in that locality, occupied by the family of one Mr. Mann, with whom he staid all night, as he could proceed no further.

Mr. Mann informed Mr. Turner that he could stop with them, but there was nothing whatever for his team and that they were but little better off in the house for anything to eat. He replied, that while he stayed he would furnish meal from his grist for them all, which he gladly did, but the steers had no supper, as they refused to eat meal.

Early the following morning he succeeded in getting his team to the opposite shore, by standing on the bank and driving it through the water. They, at first, were not inclined to go, but after a while the object was accomplished.

This part of his plan being executed, he at once began to carry out the remainder of his programme, which was to connect the two banks with some tall tree that might stand near the water's edge, on which to cross the swollen stream. Taking his axe he soon found one which he thought to be of sufficient length for the use he intended it. Quick and hard came the strokes of the axe, given with a will and by his strong vigorous arm, and soon this forest son came down with a crash into the surging water; but to his surprise it lacked much of reaching the opposite shore. He went further down the stream, made another selection which in due time shared the fate of the other tree, and again Mr. Turner was disappointed. As he followed the downward course of the river stroke after stroke, crash after crash might have been heard, and thus the day—hour by hour—wore away, and when the garments of night began to clothe the face of nature with gathering gloom, his object was not accomplished, and with no better prospects of reaching home than on the previous evening.

On returning to the crossing he found the steers had, some time during the day, recrossed the river and were now on the same side as himself and, as a matter of necessity, he stayed the second night at Mr. Mann's cabin.

Early the next morning he went two miles down the river, to Mr. Hoskins's, and procured a bundle of hay for his team and then employed his time as he had done the day before and night-fall found him again at his humble lodging place.

But Mr. Turner was not the man to get discouraged and wait for something favorable to occur; like Napoleon, he believed in creating circumstances; so, early the following morning our hero, with his purpose unchanged, went to work hopeful and with his usual determination to succeed.

At a point about three miles below the crossing he fortunately succeeded in connecting the two banks, as a reward for his perseverance. His next move was to go to Mr. Hoskins's, whom he found at home, and engaged him to drive the team through the water while he (Turner) would cross on the tree and be ready to take the steers as they reached the shore.

After some delay a crossing was effected and Mr. Turner and team reached home without any further adventure, minus his sled and grist, which he left at Mr. Mann's, to return and get as

soon as the water should subside sufficiently
to make the undertaking safe.

CHAPTER 9.

THE first settlers of Bethlehem were subjected
to the same inconvenience as all others under
like circumstances. They had no enclosed
grounds in which to pasture their cows and so
were compelled to turn them loose in the woods,
without bounds or limitations to roam at pleasure where they would. The hunting of cows in
a dense wilderness is not much like travelling for
delinquent ones in an enclosed field. To loose a
cow in the boundless forest in those days meant
a great deal. The loss of the milk to the family
was keenly felt, for they placed much reliance on
the daily produce of the cow to supply them
food in its season. It meant great anxiety on the
part of the owner, as to the length of time before she could be found, or whether she would
ever be recovered; and, if she was, might it not
be that the milk would cease to flow and they be

deprived of any further benefit from that source.

To illustrate the inconvenience of keeping stock to which the early pioneers were necessarily subjected, we give some facts relative to a genuine cow hunt.

Mr. Turner and Mr. Oakes had each a cow that ran together in the woods, coming home together at night, as a general rule; but, on one occasion, neither came and it being so near dark only a slight effort was made to find them that night. On the following morning, just at peep of day, Mr. Turner took his trusty gun and started out to search for the missing beasts. He went first to those places he thought most likely they would be, but to his surprise no trace of them could be found. During the first part of the day he confined his researches to those localities which he knew to be sometimes frequented by the cows; disappointed at not finding them, about noon he sat down to rest beneath the thick branches of a stately tree. Not expecting to be gone so long from home he had not taken the precaution to bring any food with him and having no dinner to eat and becoming somewhat anxious about the situation of things, he only stopped a short time. He now took a course that led him far from fa-

miliar scenes, examining every spot where it was
possible for the objects of his search to leave
some trace of themselves had they passed that
way, eyeing sharply the ground, taking notice of
things and flowers, hoping to find some evidence
of their whereabouts by the sides of brooks and
streamlets, on high ground and in valleys. He
continued to search until the rapidly setting sun
admonished him that the inmates of his humble
cabin would have fears that he was lost and he
must return.

But all in vain. Night was fast covering the
face of nature with its solemn grandeur, when
Mr. Turner reached his home and reported the
unfavorable results of the day's labor to his
waiting, anxious wife.

After a consultation had been held between
the two in relation to what was best to be done
under the circumstances, it was unanimously
agreed that the search must be continued.

On the following morning Mr. Turner again
started to hunt for the cows, being careful this
time to take something for a lunch; penetrating
deeper into the dense growth of timber than on
the previous day, squirrels chattered, partridges
gazed intently but shyly from some secluded cov-

ert on the strange looking intruder and a deer
bounded past him with an expression in his looks
that showed conclusively that a human being
had never before crossed his pathway and old
bruin, as if unwilling to form an acquaintance
with a strange being of whose strength he had
no knowledge and did not care to know, acted
as though he considered prudence the better part
of valor, kept out of the reach of the intruder's
gun, keeping a sharp lookout at a respectful and
safe distance.

Noon came, but the cows had not been found,
and seating himself in a cooling shade in close
proximity to a cold crystal spring he ate in a
hurry, but with good relish, his humble meal.

Having stopped about fifteen minutes he again
started, up and down, over and under huge trees
uprooted by some wild mountain storm; through
thickets and plats of tall weeds and grass; through
and around bog-holes he directed his footsteps,
looking for some sign, occasionally calling loudly
to the objects of his search, but he saw no token
of their presence and the echo of his own voice
was the only reply.

In this manner the second day of the hunt
was spent and at nightfall he returned home to

again report a failure. Thus for nine days Mr.
Turner continued to hunt for the cows. On his
return home at the close of the ninth day's search
with his usual report of "can't find them," Mr.
and Mrs. Turner held another counsel, in which
the matter was thoroughly re-examined and discussed and the conclusion reached was; "The
cows must be found, dead or alive!"

Some time during the evening the owner of
the other cow, Mr. Oakes, came in and said he
would accompany Mr. Turner in the search on
the following morning, which he did.

The reader will doubtless be curious to know
why Mr. Oakes seemed to take so little interest
in the matter, and it is but doing justice to him
that we give the reasons for his apparent indiffer-
ence. The fact that he was very busy in other
matters, besides that his cow did not give milk,
and not being particular where she was if out of
mischief and danger, and doing well, which he
was satisfied was the case with her,—provided
that she would return home when he had need
of her, about which he felt but little misgivings.
Knowing full well that she must be somewhere in
the big pasture caused him to wait and see what
would be the result of Mr. Turner's efforts.

Early next morning, which was the tenth day of the hunt, both men with their guns and an ample supply of provisions, started for the woods, and on reaching it they held a consultation as to the best way of procedure. It was finally decided to go to the Ammonoosuc River, at some point near what is now known as McGregory Hollow. Soon after reaching the point designated, they found signs of cattle having been there the night previous.

Being satisfied that the object of their search could not be far away they found the trail and hurried on, and fortunately they soon found their cows; seemingly contented and apparently none the worse for their wanderings, and the two men returned home with their runaway property and with lighter hearts than when they started at early dawn.

Under the skillful treatment of Mrs. Turner, to the surprise of all concerned, their cow was restored to her former usefulness, yielding her usual amount of milk.

CHAPTER 9.

THE wild beasts, which at first were shy, grew bolder as they became more and better acquainted with the sights and sounds of civilization. The early settlers not only made good and effectual use of their trusty guns 'to rid themselves of those troublesome enemies, but they had a cheap and efficient mode of catching bears in traps.

This trap was in form very much like a figure 4, with the top parts intersecting. It consisted of an upright standard of sufficient length to leave room for the bear to enter. This piece of wood was placed in a perpendicular position on and near the end of a large log. Another piece was placed, on the top of this upright standard, projecting beyond two feet, more or less; the other end pointing downward at an angle of about 45 degrees, of sufficient length to correspond with the general plan of the trap, the end being fashioned wedge-like. A long stick, in the side of which and near the end a notch was cut, in which was placed the lower end of the top-piece of timber. This long stick was placed a-long-side of the upright standard at about half way between its ends at which point a notch was to fit one in the long stick; on the end of this spindle (long stick) the bait was fastened. When all things were made ready they proceeded to set the machine. The framework was put together and held in position by one man, (it requiring more than one to set up a large one,) while another completed the work. This was done by placing one end of a large log on the projecting end of the top piece of timber, the other end resting on the bottom leg, the bait being turned inward, so that the bear could not reach it unless his head was beyond and toward the inside of the two logs, it being so arranged that he could not reach it from the back side.

This trap was sprung by bearing down on the bait sufficiently hard to unfasten the spindle on the upright piece, which the bear would do in removing the bait, when the top log would fall on bruin with crushing weight and he be made to suf- the extreme penalty for his reckless disregard of civilization.

In this way Mr. Turner caught many of his shaggy foes.

In the fall of the year he set one of these traps in the woods near a piece of grain to which his son Timothy, on one fine afternoon was sent to reap. He did as was directed and labored without any interruption until a noise in the woods not far distant, attracted his attention. The heavy tread and cracking of dried branches convinced young Timothy (being a small lad) that a large bear was not many rods distant. His fears were strong, but the necessity of staying to cut the grain was stronger, so he worked and watched till it was time to return to the house which he did much quicker than he had been in the habit of doing, and immediately made a report of what he had heard while at work in the field.

The father was satisfied that it was a bear that had made the noise and remembering his plan, started out to investigate, and on reaching the spot he found bruin fast in his trap.

On one occasion a bear had remained so long in the trap that it could not be disposed of in the usual manner. So Mr. Turner concluded to give it to his hogs, he having a number of them at that time, and he proceeded at once to carry his plan into execution by throwing the meat into the yard where he kept his swine; but, to his astonishment, instead of its being received with gladness, it disturbed their equanimity. They showed their displeasure, first, by sly looks and low grunts, which increased in dimensions until every hog seemed to be doing his very best to increase the uproar and confusion,—running, jumping, and squealing as if impelled by an unseen power. Crazed by fright, and mad—frantic from their own unearthly noise—they, as if by mutual agreement, decided to leave that terrible place and bursting through the strong fence that surrounded the enclosure, scattered in all directions.

It was now Mr. Turner's time to be alarmed for the safety of his valuable property, for there was great danger that they might take to the woods and escape beyond the power of recovery, but by much coaxing and labor they were all restored to their proper place and usual quietness again prevailed among the inmates of Mr. Turner's hog-yard.

But one thing is certain, his hogs never had another opportunity to dine on bear meat.

There is an incident connected with one of his log bear traps which is worth relating, because of the moral lesson it teaches.

An old fox in his ramblings chanced one day to be rusticating in that vicinity and, illured by the tempting bait, he thought it a good time to lunch; so, after closely scrutinizing the locality, his foxship walked leisurely in and helped himself. The bait being turned so far inward and the fox so much smaller than a bear that when in a position to dine he was beyond harm, being to the one side of the trap. He was enjoying his meal with a good relish when, evidently, the trap was on the point of springing, when seeing the motion of the top log (being on the alert for mischief,) he started to retrace his steps and reached the fatal spot just in time to receive the full force of the descending, crushing weight.

Had he quietly remained and finished his repast he might have left the spot unharmed and with a satisfied appetite have gone on his way rejoicing.

Moral: Acting from impulse, minus judgment, may bring fatal results, and there is such a thing as being too smart.

CHAPTER 10.

One of the many ills to which flesh is heir to, is, methinks, the toothache. Who can describe it, or to what can it be likened? What language can be found that will truthfully convey the real feelings of the unpleasant sufferer? One who never experienced its effect, both on the mind and body, is not qualified to give an authorized opinion on the subject. As a general rule it has no respect of person. From the highest officer in the government down to the lowest serf or most degraded beggar, it makes its unwelcome visits sooner or later and on that dreadful occasion the general expression is, "Oh! how my tooth does ache." Sometimes the pain continues as if having no disposition to stop or in no hurry to cease tormenting its victim, again as if to make haste and bring matters to a speedy close or to try its power in another form the pain comes and goes by jumps. Its effect on different dispositions is truly surprising, for the best of people with a mild and gentle temper may lose their equanimity of mind, but what shall be said of the irritable and fractious? Only this: It certainly makes no visible improvement on their use of language, manners or general deportment. It is not for us to investigate the cause of the various kinds and form of toothaches, but only state the fact that Mr. Turner had the toothache in its worst and most perplexing manner, and if he would have the trouble removed by having the diseased part extracted, three conditions must be complied with: a disposition to go, sufficient time in which to go, and then to go and have it taken out.

The point of time in which everything was in readiness for the operation was in the middle of the night, and surely the aspect seemed gloomy enough — toothache within and inky darkness without—which circumstances did not conspire to make him hopeful, or his prospective journey cheerful or pleasant.

Taking a blazing torch, to prevent his losing his way, he was soon on his mission, the objective point being a house on West Hill; where resided a man who sometimes acted the part of the dentist. His instruments were of the most approved ancient style, the modern instruments in dentistry not being in use.

The torch which Mr. Turner carried was not only of service to him in directing his footsteps but it kept the wild inmates of the forest at a proper distance. So deep was the darkness that his glaring light hardly penetrated the thick gloom, beyond his immediate presence. The movement of the light showed that though careful as he endeavored to be, he would frequently step from the path to one side or the other, and its unsteady motion revealed the fact that the toe of his boot now and then came in contact with some unseen obstacle—a protruding stump of some small sapling or treacherous projecting root.

Under these vexed circumstances our hero was slowly but surely making progress westward with that mental activity natural to one in like condition, his thoughts and feelings occasionally finding vent in expressions like the following: "How my tooth aches! hope I shall find him at home." Just at this moment an inquisitive owl, perched on an old stub in close proximity, being disturbed in his midnight reveries by the glaring torch and, as if catching the last words of the intruder—"find him at home!"—and curious to know who this "him" was with whom this stranger could have business at the hour of midnight, unceremoniously disturbed the pervading solemnity of the night by making the forest echo, " Who, who, who, who! "

This night bird continued to repeat his saucy question, while Mr. Turner as persistently refused to notice the interrogator, his mind being fixed on his aching tooth and the dentist.

In due time the inmates of a dwelling on West Hill were disturbed in the midst of pleasant dreams by a loud rap on the door. Fortunately, the Doctor was at home, and in a few minutes the aching tooth was removed, root and branch, and Mr. Turner returned home in season to get a pleasant morning nap.

CHAPTER II.

Although Mr. Turner was successful generally in his various undertakings, accumulating considerable property, yet in some things he was unfortunate.

He bought the land on which he settled, and paid for it, but subsequently it was ascertained that his title was worthless and, not wishing to change his place of residence, he paid for his farm the second time.

We refer to one more instance of a like kind, showing his financial misfortunes. The idea of making a turnpike road through Bethlehem was conceived, it being clearly seen that for years a large business would be transacted between the merchants at Portland, Maine, and the people of northern New Hampshire and eastern part of the Green Mountain State, and that the many teams necessarily engaged in carrying the trade would most naturally find their way through this town, and subsequent events proved the correctness of this idea.

To carry out the plan of making Bethlehem a great thoroughfare of business a company was legally formed—or it had that appearance to the outside world—and Mr. Turner took the job of building a part of this turnpike. He built it according to contract, hiring help to the amount of two hundred dollars, but the expense incurred by him in constructing the road the company never paid one cent,—having lost its identity, if ever had any real existence.

The amount lost by a worthless title to his land and his expense in constructing the turnpike was a great misfortune to Mr. Turner, for let it be remembered that the loss of a few hundred dollars in those days and under difficult circumstances was much greater than the loss of a like sum at the present time.

Mr. Turner ended his earthly pilgrimage in Bethlehem at the age of 73 years, on the farm where he made his settlement in 1790. He was father of Timothy P. Turner, a much esteemed citizen who represented the town in the councils of State, being father of Mr. James N. Turner, the proprietor of a pleasant summer boarding house situated on the old homestead farm.

In June, 1803, an accident occurred that brought feelings of sadness to the whole town. Isaac Batchellor and Aaron Kenney were shingling a barn on what is known as the Lot Woodbury farm, now occupied by Harrison Sawyer. While at work another man came on the roof, and the additional weight thereby caused the staging to give way, precipitating the three persons to the ground. The visitor and Mr. Kenney were not dangerously injured,—catching hold of some parts of the staging in their descent the force of the concussion was lessened. Mr. Bachellor was not so fortunate. With no impediment to obstruct his descent he fell on the rocks below with great force.

Dr. Burns of Littleton, was sent for in great haste, but on his arrival at the place of disaster he found the unfortunate man had breathed his last.

There was one incident that added solemnity to the presence of death.

While the men were busy at their work there was a rapidly gathering storm in the far off western sky, a long black mass of rising clouds skirted the distant horizon; peal on peal of cracking, rolling thunder moved in all its native grandeur, amid the distant storm, while the vivid lightning played its wild fantastic part in the general confusion of waring elements, assuming an appearance of vast sheets of fire, as it moved in a serpentine manner along the angry billowy pile. Nearer and nearer came the shower, quicker and heavier fell the descending hammers, while the grand old forest awake to the increasing interest of the moment, sent back its echoes with increasing rapidity.   At this juncture the staking broke and with fatal results.

About the time Mr. Batchellor breathed his last the storm burst on the solemn scene in all the wild fury of a mountain shower.   Death within the dwelling, with its ghastly form, combined with the noise of the roaring raging elements without, all conspired to make the scene a fearful and impressive one.

Thus the living were brought face to face with that great mystery so much alike to all mankind.

The educated and illiterate, alike, gaze earnestly and wishfully (as they stand on the border of the known,) towards the boundless unknown beyond, with doubtful forebodings, and the mystery is no nearer solved than it was before.   While reason and revelation only comparatively reduces the darkness into twilight, enabling man to quite distinctly discern some essential features of a future life, there are very many things which we would be glad to learn that are veiled by impenetrable blackness.

Isaac Batchellor is no more; but his good character and worthy deeds are a lasting monument of his unselfishness and high esteem in which he was held by all who knew him.   He was father of Stillman Batchellor, who died in Bethlehem, and who was the father of Albert Batchellor, a rising young lawyer in his profession, now located in Littleton, N. H.

CHAPTER 12.

THE liability to be lost in the woods was greater in those early days than now. Even the most experienced, in woodcraft and accustomed for many long years to a forest life, would sometimes find themselves so bewildered in the bowers of nature as to be unable to discern the four cardinal points of the compass, mistaking one for the other, believing that every stream of water they saw run exactly the reverse from what it really did. Men who would have laughed at the idea of being lost where they felt so well acquainted and were so much at home, found themselves so entangled that they could not be extricated without outside aid.

We will relate an instance of that kind.

Bruin was very much annoyed at his future prospects, for civilization was rapidly destroying his cherished home, driving him further and further away from his delightful, chosen retreat; taking from him, by force, the land and forests to which he had an undoubted title by rightful inheritance. But the cool, calculating brain of man was too much for the instinctive power of his noble bearship; he saw the constantly increasing number of the invading foe without being able to prevent it. This he *could do*, and *did*, shared with them their crops, lambs, and whatever else could be of use to him, thus making the bold intruder pay rent for occupying his majesty's beautiful, and productive domain.

On the other hand the settlers claimed the right to all of nature's vast and delightful ground, and the right to cultivate where, and as much of the same as they chose; and not only this but to catch and kill every bear, great and small, that they could. This state of feelings caused an unceasing warfare between the parties interested which would most surely end in the almost entire extermination of the shaggy beasts.

A man by the name of John Bemis who resided in Littleton, in what is now known as the

Towne's neighborhood, had a piece of growing corn to which a bear took a great liking, and he went about the work of securing by stealth his part of the golden kernel before its harvest time.

Mr. Bemis soon discovered the plot, and at once determined to punish, if possible, the daring thief; for the selfish creature showed no disposition to make a fair division of the much desired treasure, but on the contrary seemed inclined to appropriate it all to his own use. Accordingly, he so arranged a trap that he was quite positive ere long he could bring old bruin to summary punishment, he having already been tried and convicted, the only remaining part of the programme being to catch and kill him.

Everything was now ready to carry his plan into execution. Mr. Bemis went to and from his trap, but found no prisoner, Bruin continued to visit the corn-field about his accustomed business, regardless of what his bitter foe might think or do. But the monotony of the general aspects of affairs was suddenly broken. One morning as usual, Mr. Bemis went to look at his trap and found that it was gone. The truth at once flashed across his mind; the trap had done its part of

the work faithfully, but the fastenings had not
been made sufficiently strong, and the bear had
escaped taking it along with him.

The neighbors were soon informed of the true
state of things and having a common interest in
the matter, they unhesitatingly agreed to make
it a common cause and to go immediately in
search of the culprit. With Mr. Bemis they
soon started on the hunt.

This was on the morning of October 9, 1804.
Mr. Bemis, not anticipating a long search, started
before eating his morning meal, taking with him
his little dog and gun, expecting soon to return.
Being lame he could not keep up with the rest of
the party, and soon finding himself left beyond
the other hunters' call took the way that seemed
to him the most advisable. From that time he
saw no more of his companions until found by
them in a sad condition.

The weather signs of the morning were ominous of a coming storm. The low distant sound
of murmuring thunder was born from afar on a
passing breeze, while the distant stifled noise of
the restless elements, like some mighty giant
putting forth all his strength to free himself from
some galling chain, ready to snap asunder at

every successive attempt to extricate himself, was indistinctly heard from away to the westward.

Mr. Bemis moved on and the clouds continued to thicken as the storm gathered. In a short time the rattling thunder and vivid flash, accompanied with a heavy fall of rain, was followed by a calm, which showed that the storm had done its work in that locality and passed on its way to visit the mountains. When it ceased to rain the snow began to fall and continued till the ground was covered to the depth of about twelve inches. When the rain began to descend Mr. Bemis sought shelter beneath some friendly covert and there remained until the calm that followed the shower; then he again resumed his search and commenced to shout for his companions, but no answer came,—echo being the only reply.

It now became evident to him that he had better return home; having thus decided he commenced as he supposed a homeward journey with his thoughts on the occurrences of the day. He moved on not doubting but what he would reach home in due time in safety, but to his astonishment the coming night began to wrap

her sable curtains around hilltops and valley,
warning him that greater darkness and increasing cold would soon surround him. And those
loved ones at home were waiting and watching
eagerly for his return. He now increased his
exertions expecting every moment to hit some
familiar spot from whence he could make a start
in the right direction, for he now saw that he
had lost the points of compass, for had he gone
towards home he would have reached it long before that time.

Feeling assured that he did not know what
course to follow after a while he concluded to
make the best of his unpleasant situation and
finding the best shelter that the unfavorable circumstances would allow of, weary and hungry he
halted for the night; but being used to the
woods he expected to reach home on the morrow in time to eat an early breakfast with his
now anxious family.

With these thoughts he yielded to the imperative demands of nature and was lost to his dangerous situation in the close embrace of welcomed sleep.

Leaving the unfortunate man unconscious of
what was transpiring around him, we turn our

attention to his friends and neighbors. Hope
and fear, each in turn filled his family with conflicting emotion; the liabilities and probabilities
were freely discussed, and the circumstances favorable for and against his safe return were
weighed with deep feelings experienced only under a like condition of things. While now and
then some one of their number would exclaim,
"Hark! I hear footsteps; guess he has come."
But it was all an illusion born of the wish that it
might be so.

Thus the long night of suspense wore slowly
away with those anxious ones.

When morning dawned the men in that settlement having been informed that Mr. Bemis had
not returned to his home, prepared to search for
him.   Everything being ready the party started
for the forest taking dinner horns, dogs and guns.
When at a given point the men blew their horns
and discharged their guns, which caused the
dogs to set up a vigorous and prolonged whining
and barking; then separating, as marked out by
a previous programme, the search was continued
throughout the day, occasionally halting to shout
at the top of their voices the name of the lost
man, to which was added the sound of horns and

barking of dogs. This mingling of discordant sounds when blended into one confused mass made the welkin ring with an indescribable noise that reached the ears of distant listeners in a wild fantastic manner, disturbing numberless slumbering echoes, frightening wild beasts from their hiding places, and birds of various kinds sought safety on the wing as if conscious of some impending danger. At nightfall they all returned home with sorrowful hearts to report that their efforts to find Mr. Bemis had proved a failure.

Hope, that bright angel of mercy that hitherto had been a constant companion with the disconsolate and afflicted family, whispered words of cheer and brighter anticipations; thus, to some extent, lessening the sadness of the hour, now ceased to be regarded, its soothing voice being lost in the thickening darkness of fear that pervaded their hearts and with which the very atmosphere seemed to be impregnated.

We now return to Mr. Bemis who, when daylight appeared, came from the place where he had stayed the previous night. Faint with hunger and worn with the labor and excitement of the preceding day, he started with his faithful dog, as he supposed in a homeward direction; but on reaching the Ammonoosuc River he discovered his mistake; and he was still farther deceived in thinking the river before him was John's River, and that it ran in the opposite direction from what it really did.

This was a fatal mistake, for had he followed the stream downward he would soon have found the abode of man; but in going up the river he penetrated deeper and deeper into the forests of Bethlehem. He spent the day in wandering and resting and when night came on he was still beyond the reach of human aid, and seating himself beneath the friendly branches of the nearest tree he went to sleep. Thus ended the second day of his absence from home.

After the friends of Mr. Bemis had returned from their fruitless search, they held a council and it was decided to resume the search for him on the following day, which they did, their company being enlarged by additional numbers, using the same means as the day before to ascertain the whereabouts of the object of their search with no better results.

The movements of Mr. Bemis on this day were similar to those of the day previous, he

growing more weary and confused, having less
and less comprehension of his real situation.
Travelling more in circles, coming back to his
starting point, at the same time moving somewhat higher up the river. Nature could endure
no more for the time and he sank down upon the
earth exhausted. A little sleep revived him, but
on the following morning the once strong mind
and body was deranged and weak, yet he continued to wander about stopping often to rest
and then to move again. Too much overcome
with hunger, fatigue and exposure to have any
well devised plan, only a vague idea that he was
lost seemed to inspire him and he must go home.
Thus he traveled having no regard as to where
or in what direction.

After the second day was ended it was decided
that the search should be continued until the
lost man should be found, dead or alive as might
be.

By this time the news that a man was lost in
the forest had spread far and wide. On the next
day the number of men that joined in the search
was greatly augmented, and the manner of procedure was similar to that of the preceding days,
only, if possible, the party shouted more earnest-

ly, blew their horns with greater rigor, and the guns were made to speak more loudly. Suddenly some of the men were attracted by the barking of a dog belonging to the party, and on going to the spot discovered the lost man.

When found Mr. Bemis was sitting on a log holding his gun. Examination showed his powder was wet and the flint of his gun lost, leaving him without the means to kill game or make a fire; his feet were badly frozen and he had eaten nothing since leaving home, excepting a piece of his dog's tongue, the remainder of which was found in his pocket.

The shock which Mr. Bemis received by this sad event caused his death about seven years later.

The place where Mr. Bemis was found was in the vicinity of Alder Brook, on what is now known as Platt's Meadow.

CHAPTER 13.

THE wants and needs of the early settlers were unlike in amount and kind, in many respects, to those of to-day, and their manner of securing the necessaries of life corresponded with their surroundings. Their food was of the plainest kind, anything eatable being gladly welcomed. The texture and cut of their wearing apparel was in harmony with their idea of durability, convenience and comfort. The animal, vegetable and mineral kingdoms were put under contribution and every thing within their reach utilized to the best advantage. Costly ornaments and silk dresses as well as the luxuries known to older communities had no place in their humble homes. The heavy growth of timber was made to serve a purpose, in a manner not practical now, neither would it be available at the present time. From early dawn to a late hour at night there might have been seen from various localities the curling smoke making its way above the surrounding tree tops. A visit to the spot would reveal the reason why it was so, and also afford a practical illustration of salts making.   There would be one or more men busy in rolling great hardwood logs on a large pile, on one side of which the fire was fast converting the once standing trees into ashes, while close by would be seen large kettles in which alkali was boiling and foaming, having been obtained by leaching the ashes secured after the logs had been burned, · as a row of tubs or old barrels near by indicated.

The salts obtained by boiling were sent to market, in exchange for which they would receive the necessaries of life.   In various localities small mounds, made of ashes leached by the salt makers may now be seen.   On the Joel Winch place, near the line that separated that from Mr. Turner's, was a building where salts were manufactured from ashes bought of all who chose to sell them.

One incident in salts making that has been handed down to the present generation, we give as an echo from the past.   One of the salt makers returned home at night for his supper, taking good care to have his trusty rifle in readiness for use at a moment's warning, as he had seen a bear a number of times in that vicinity.

It was dark when he set out on his return. The surrounding gloom and thoughts of bruin had worked his imagination into so lively a condition that he would not have been disappointed in seeing game at any time. With this state of feelings he came in sight of his place of work and suddenly halted; the dim light of fire gave surrounding objects an indistinct appearance, which combined with an excited brain, brought him to the conclusion that his shaggy enemy had, in his absence, taken the liberty to gratify his majesty's curiosity by making an examination of things in general, and, bringing his rifle to his shoulder, his eye rested along the barrel till it reached the unconscious object of his gaze, when a sharp report broke the pervading stillness of the place. Drawing his long knife to finish the ugly brute if not already dead, he rushed to the spot and to his surprise found what he supposed to be a bear was a kettle which he sometimes used in boiling alkali, but at that time it was not in use, which fact he did not realize when he discharged his rifle. Being a good marksman the ball had hit the mark so squarely that it destroyed its future usefulness. But he had this consolation,—if it had been a bear he would have been sure of his hide and also the bounty.

The great suffering arising from the need of proper and sufficient food, and the importance of making salts in connection with obtaining it, is illustrated by the following incident :

When the bridge which the town voted to build was in process of construction, some of the workmen were obliged to labor continually in the water, with nothing to eat during the day, but warm milk porridge brought to them by their families.   This extremity to which the citizens of Bethlehem were forced, resulted in discontinuing the building of the bridge for the time and to keep themselves from starving, they went to making salts.   When a sufficient amount had been manufactured it was sent to market a distance of about 170 miles, with an ox team. The people during the time it took to go to market and return (which was nearly a month) subsisted to some extent on boiled roots, and indeed everything that could afford them nourishment.

CHAPTER 14.

THE inhabitants of Bethlehem resided so far from any post office and the facilities for distributing mail matter were sobad that the newspapers were delivered at the homes of those who took them, by special arrangement outside of the post office department, the cost of which was paid by the subscribers.

The first person employed to act on this plan was Reuben Baker, then a boy, and who now resides in town. He obtained the papers in the town of Barnet, Vermont, and in connection with this, he did errands of various kinds and any other business that different inhabitants desired.

A serious accident would have befallen a man near Bethlehem street, but for the fortunate fact that the center of gravity was on the side of the horse opposite the danger. The man rode into town and after gratifying his desire for toddy and flip (his favorite kinds of drink) to an inordinate extent, it being near dark, he mounted his horse with some assistance and started home-

ward, but a muddled brain and an unsteady hand
guided his horse into an adjoining field in which
was a deep well around which there was no curb.
In that direction horse and rider went unconscious of any danger until they had reached a
point so close to the well that one stirrup of the
saddle hung directly over the edge of the yawn-
ing abyss, when the rider lost his balance and
fell to the ground on the side of the horse far-
thest from the excavation. In his descent his
boot was left behind and, as if disliking the turn
events had taken, as soon as it was freed from
the foot and stirrup it fell into the dark depth
below. Search was made for the missing boot,
but its whereabouts remained a mystery until after a time it became necessary to clean out the
well, when, at the bottom, the article that disappeared so mysteriously on that eventful evening,
was found.

Accidents of various kinds with more or less
serious results, occupy a place in the early history of this locality. It was during one of these
extremely cold days of winter that sometimes
come to our northern clime, that a man with an
ox team arrived in front of a tavern on West
Hill, kept by Thornton Barrett (now owned by

Luther Wallace,) being very cold he left his team in the road and went in to warm himself by a blazing fire and take something to cheer his drooping spirits.

Mr. Barrett had the reputation of being well provided with good fuel and that wonderful working drink "that warms a man in winter and cools him in summer."

How long he stayed is uncertain, but when he was ready to depart he started out and coming in sight of his team which had not moved from where he left it, he gave in a sharp, loud voice the command, "Wake up my boys and go along there!" Perceiving that they took no notice of what he said, he started towards them, repeating the command with some additional exclamations and adjectives in a more vehement manner, but with no better results.

On reaching his team he found his cattle dead, they having died from cold while standing in their tracks.

CHAPTER 15.

THE first resident shoemaker in town was Moses Eastman, who resided on the farm now occupied by Amasa Streeter. The first blacksmith was Abel Hale, whose shop was located on the ground now covered by the Sinclair House. The first regular physician by profession in town was Peter Shattuck, but he did not practic medicine. The first practicing physician was a Mr. Rawson, who resided on West Hill opposite the spot where stood for many years the school house in District No. 4. The first grist mill was located at McGregory Hollow, Stephen Houghton, proprietor. Two churches were erected not long after the town was organized. The Congregational building was located near where now stands the beautiful Centennial House; the Free Will Baptist building was located about a mile farther west on the main road nearly opposite the residence of Timothy Hildreth and his son Orville, at the junction of the two roads.

After these places of worship had served the purpose first intended, they were disposed of in the following manner: The first was sold and used for various building purposes, it being very commodious the amount of timber was large. The other was taken down and transformed into a starch factory, and located near the main street, on the stream once known as Bean Brook near Reuben Baker's residence, where it now remains. On that stream and in the same vicinity there once existed a mill for grinding provender, a threshing machine moved by water power, a blacksmith shop, clover-seed mill and chair factory (some of the chairs there manufactured are now in existence,) and a brick yard.

Then, as now, officers of justice were on the alert to punish offenders of the law. The following is an incident connected with the administration of justice at the time of which we now write. One Dutton, for not doing as the law required was duly arrested at the proper time and in an official manner by Stephen Houghton, constable, who politely informed the prisoner that his presence at Haverhill jail was very desirable and that as he was somewhat interested in the affair, and, to be sure that he, Dutton, was not prevented by some unforseen event from reaching the place he, Houghton, would escort him hither.

Apparently by mutual consent the two started for their place of destination. At the close of the first day's journey they reached the home of Caleb Baker, a merchant in Franconia, distant five miles from Bethlehem. Here the evening was spent in a jovial manner—telling stories and relating incidents in their individual lives—the prisoner taking part in the conversation.

Everything progressed finely until the time to retire had arrived, when the question arose, "What shall be done with Mr. Dutton?"

To answer this grave question in a legal way puzzled the officer. How to sleep and keep a sharp lookout for the prisoner at the same time was a task beyond his comprehension.

Some said one thing, some another; several plans were discussed, when one mind more fertile than the rest, said he had a feasible way of fixing things all right, and this was his plan.

In the room was a very large cradle having no footboard, in which Mr. Dutton was to be placed and securely bound. All agreed· that this was just the thing to be done, wondering why it had not been thought of before.

By this mode the prisoner would be placed beyond the power of escape, besides securing comfortable quarters, an opportunity for a short sleep and pleasant dreams,—at least so thought the officer of justice.

The scheme executed to the apparent satisfaction of all interested, officer Houghton waited until a deep sonorous sound from the cradle announced his presence no longer necessary with his prisoner. His physical and mental powers beginning to feel the effects of the great strain to which they had been subjected through the day, and the reaction that sooner or later comes to all minds wrought up to a high pitch by external and internal causes, beginning to manifest itself, he arose from his sitting posture and taking one searching look at the place from whence came the sound, now changed to such loud heavy snoring as to be almost frightful. At which point the old family clock chimed its hourly music with a satisfied air announcing twelve o'clock. All was well and he retired. He was soon sleeping only as one can who needs rest and is conscious of having faithfully performed his duty.

All continued to slumber peacefully until the day dawned when Mr. Dutton awoke much re-

freshed by the repose he had enjoyed. Everything was still and he was alone. After a few
moments reflection he thus soliloquized: "I have
no desire to escape; but if I could play a practical joke on my keeper and make him an object
of laughter, placing him in a position where he
would feel compelled to pay certain bills I would
very much like to do it, for, in that case, I would
share in the fun and receive tangible proof of
the benefit to be derived from the execution of
such a movement. But, should I be detected
and fail, the laugh would be turned on myself
and I be obliged to pay the necessary expenses."
After a moment's pause, he added, "Yes, I will
try it, and run the risk, for in either case I shall
get a drink!"

The cradle, though a large one, was short com-
pared with the length of the occupant, his feet
protruding far beyond the end of his prison
house he could not extricate himself from his
fastenings without arousing the family and thus
frustrate his plans; but he could leave and take
his prison with him.

As every moment's delay endangered the success of his scheme he immediately got to his feet
and noiselessly moved out of the house.

A few rods distant from the house a secluded spot afforded him the necessary retreat, and here we leave him to return to his official majesty.

Hardly had Dutton ensconced himself and the shrubbery ceased to move when an inmate of the family came tripping along, pail in hand, bound for the spring. About the same time Mr. Houghton arose from his bed, hastily dressed and, with a serene and placid countenance, went to give a morning salutation to his friend Dutton.

On opening the door of the apartment wher he had left the prisoner only a few hours before, with one foot on the threshold he stopped in blank amazement, for the culprit was nowhere to be seen. Was he dreaming, in a nightmare, or was it a reality? At that moment the loud noise of swallows in the capacious old-fashioned chimney attracted his attention in that direction and he would have made an examination of that locality but for the fact which he now for the first time seemed to realize, that the cradle was gone as well as prisoner; surely both could not be in that sooty aperture.

The calmness that sat enthroned on his hopeful visage but a few moments previous had now disappeared. Hope and fear alternately occupied a place in his disturbed mind, occasionally blending together in one confused mass making his situation no enviable one.

"Yes, he has vanished, and I, officer Houghton am responsible; but he must be found." The alarm was given, and search immediately commenced. All were animated by the event: great excitement prevailed; men, women and children were on the alert running hither and thither, some giving their opinions quite freely in the matter, while others were silently endeavoring to find the trail, were scrutinizing every nook and corner, when suddenly a shout was heard followed by the declaration that made the welkin ring, "We have found him!"

Soon all gathered at the spot to find Mr. Dutton as quiet and undisturbed as though nothing unusual had occurred, at the same time, remarking, "I was enjoying life very much, and cannot comprehend the necessity for so much noise and confusion solely on my account."

He had come to that spot for a little out door exercise and change of atmosphere, and that he would have returned in due time alone; but, uner the circumstances, he would go with the crowd.

Rising to his feet he returned to the house as he left it, with the cradle on his back, saying as he did so, in his most polite off-handed way, "Mr. Houghton, Sir, officer of justice: I think that it is your treat!"

The game had been successfully played and Dutton had won. Amid shouts and laughter, in which all joined, they returned back and . as expected, Mr. Houghton regarded it as a good joke and acted well his part in the closing scene.

The matter was settled on the spot and the two returned home together, leaving on record the fact that one man had literally taken up his bed and walked.

CHAPTER 16.

CONTRASTING Bethlehem, as it was nearly one hundred years ago, with what it now is we can hardly realize the fact that from so small a beginning has been developed our prosperous and flourishing condition. To say that wealth has done all this is to defame the time-honored memory of our worthy ancestors and do great injustice to the honest laboring men of Bethlehem of to-day. It puts in the background intelligence, morality and Christianity—elements ever essential to success. It ignores the fact that wealth is only an instrument in accomplishing high and noble purposes. It disregards prominent facts in our history, as though undisputed records of the past could be blotted out of existence by an empty, pompous assertion. It seeks to change the order of things established by the Creator, and to found prosperity on an entirely new basis. Such an idea is born of ignorance, with no true conception of the nature of true greatness or the mode of obtaining it.

Those who assert that wealth is the highest point to reach the one great object of life, reiterates the sentiments of Mr. Hammond of South Carolina, when he said of the laboring portion of the community, "They are the mud-sills of society!"

An attempt to enforce this theory has brought into existence secret organizations which honeycombed the nations of the East and made insecure the despotic governments of the old world, and like causes would produce like results in our own happy land.

The foundation of what Bethlehem now is and what she is capable of being was laid deep on broad principles that exist in the nature of things, unaccompanied by wealth and the many luxuries of a later date, but under a condition of things the reverse of all this. The germ of its greatness was planted beneath overhanging branches of forest trees, among granite rocks and piles of snow attended by piercing blasts from the frozen clime. It was fostered and cared for amid the gloom of poverty as well as great perils and hardships, and at times with many fears of starvation. It was watered by many tears that often times flowed like summer's rain to invigorate the tender plant destined to unfold its branches and bear its legitimate fruitage far down the pathway of time. Certain fundamental principles underlie prosperity and true greatness and are essential elements of success at all times and in all parts of the globe, whether surrounded with palm and cocoa trees, in the land of orange blossoms, of cotton and of cane, or among the granite hills of our New England homes. Industry in the right direction has acted a conspicuous part in the growth of Bethlehem, from the day the woodman's axe broke the silence of the dense forests of Lloyd's Hill to the present time. Economy also takes its place as a valuable feature in the great whole, to which much credit is due, while the school and meeting houses truly proclaim: "Without our aid the present condition of things could not have been what they now are." The seed of prosperity was sown by other hands, we reap the harvest: they planted the tree, we gather the fruit thereof. It is not for this generation to lay the foundation, but it is our duty to defend and, by our individual efforts, aid in strengthening that glorious structure, the building of which was commenced by our worthy ancestors nearly one hundred years ago on the site of our pleasantly situated and beautiful mountain homes.

BETHLEHEM AT THE PRESENT TIME.

Bethlehem village is situated upon a high pla-
teau nearly 1500 feet above the level of the sea,
with mountains fringing the horizon in every direction. Thousands of people visit this place
annually to enjoy its beautiful scenery and in-
vigorating air. Some of the best views in the
world are obtained from Bethlehem, and the
cars can be seen almost any day ascending Mt.
Washington. The town is supplied with never-
failing spring water, brought from a high hill
back of the village. The drainage is perfect.

There are about thirty hotels and boarding
houses, a public hall, three miles of sidewalks
and all necessary improvements. Being situated
midway between the White and Franconia
Mountains every point of interest can be visited
in a day's excursion.

Tourists visiting Bethlehem should come on
the P. & O. R. R. or the B. C. & M. and White
Mountains R. R. to Bethlehem Junction and
there take the Narrow Gauge Road to the village.
Those coming over the B. C. & M. R. R. can take

the stage at Littleton and reach Bethlehem 20 minutes in advance of railroad time.

Below is a list of the principal hotels and boarding houses

Maplewood,—one of the largest and handsomest buildings of its kind about the mountains; accommodates 500 guests. Maplewood Cottage accommodates 100, and Maplewood Hall 150. These three houses are all under one ownership. The Sinclair House covers the site of the original establishment—the first of its kind in Bethlehem —accommodates 300 guests. Blandin House, H. C. Clark, proprietor, accommodates 30 guests ; Centennial House, H. W. Wilder, proprietor, 60 guests; Mt. Agassiz House, H. Nye, proprietor, 60; Mt. Washington House, C. L. Bartlett, proprietor, 60; Prospect House, G. W. Phillips, proprietor, 80; Ranlet's Hotel, D. W. Ranlet, proprietor, 75; Turner House, J. N. Turner & Son, proprietors, 75. The Highland House, the Bellevue, the Alpine, · the Uplands, the Bethlehem House, the Howard and the Strawberry Hill Houses each accommodate from 50 to 150 guests.

There are numerous smaller houses at which guests can secure good accommodations at reasonable rates.

All these houses have good livery stables connected where fine teams can be obtained to visit
any of the various points of interest, and return
the same day.

Taking everything into consideration, Bethlehem offers better advantages to the summer tou-
rist than almost any place on the western conti-
nent.

The Narrow Gauge Railroad from Bethlehem
Junction,—which runs to the Profile House, also
to Bethlehem street,—is a great accommodation
to travelers.

Many fine private residences have been erected
in this town in the past few years, among which
is one built the present season on West Hill,
and which is probably the most oddly constructed private residence in New England.

During the month of August 2,000 summer
boarders have comfortable rooms in this town.

The population of Bethlehem is 1,400.

Milton Keynes UK
Ingram Content Group UK Ltd.
UKHW040930180224
437992UK00003B/149

9 783385 332430